21 +17 — **38**	46 +12 —	53 +14 —	15 +62 —	75 +13 —	+41 —	+14 —
40 +25 —	27 +10 —	30 +50 —	18 +60 —	40 +40 —	39 +50 —	34 +34 —
26 +33 —	18 +61 —	44 +24 —	62 +37 —	73 +25 —	34 +55 —	51 +38 —

Add 16 to 33 = [**49**]   50 + 40 = [   ]   20 + 65 = [   ]

25 more than 54 = [   ]   Add 30 to 30 = [   ]   17 plus 61 = [   ]

3 + 8 = [**11**]	6 + 5 = [ ]	5 + 8 = [ ]	1 + 9 = [ ]
9 + 6 = [ ]	8 + 7 = [ ]	4 + 10 = [ ]	10 + 7 = [ ]
5 + 7 = [ ]	6 + 8 = [ ]	7 + 6 = [ ]	55 + 9 = [ ]
2 + 8 = [ ]	9 + 9 = [ ]	5 + 10 = [ ]	7 + 7 = [ ]

3 7 +8 — **18**	4 9 +6 —	3 1 +9 —	5 5 +7 —	2 7 +8 —	3 5 +7 —	5 9 +1 —
7 4 +5 —	8 6 +3 —	4 5 +9 —	5 6 +8 —	3 6 +9 —	2 9 +8 —	6 6 +6 —
6 8 +7 —	9 4 +9 —	8 7 +6 —	6 9 +9 —	9 8 +6 —	8 8 +7 —	5 9 +8 —

Number +

5	7	3	9	38	29	44
+26	+15	+48	+52	+ 7	+ 5	+ 8
31						

36	54	75	28	66	83	49
+ 7	+ 8	+ 9	+ 5	+ 8	+ 9	+ 6

Add 36 to 9 = | **45** | 7 more than 25 = | | 6 plus 47 = |

4 more than 28 = | | 9 plus 54 = | | Add 8 to 65 = |

35	16	12	19	46	64	58
+17	+58	+49	+38	+16	+19	+17

25	38	36	55	47	67	38
+35	+42	+27	+29	+29	+27	+59

3	6	5	29	35	4	7
7	8	9	3	6	48	9
+25	+34	+21	+ 7	+ 5	+ 2	+33
35						

26	34	53	47	59	37	68
9	27	8	18	28	46	9
+15	+ 6	+19	+ 6	+ 6	+ 8	+19

62	34	43	27	26	36	15
18	25	27	26	49	39	29
+19	+16	+19	+38	+15	+27	+36

What is the total of 4, 6 and 18? | | Fifty-three add thirty-nine | |

Number −

10 − 2 --- **8**	12 − 3 ---	11 − 4 ---	10 − 5 ---	12 − 7 ---	11 − 7 ---	10 − 6 ---
14 − 9 ---	13 − 6 ---	16 − 7 ---	15 − 8 ---	18 − 9 ---	13 − 8 ---	17 − 8 ---
20 −14 ---	30 −26 ---	40 −32 ---	30 −21 ---	20 −18 ---	50 −45 ---	40 −37 ---
30 −24 ---	60 −57 ---	40 −35 ---	70 −63 ---	50 −48 ---	80 −72 ---	60 −51 ---
20 − 5 ---	40 −22 ---	30 −14 ---	50 −35 ---	70 −53 ---	60 −47 ---	40 −25 ---
32 −13 --- **19**	35 −16 ---	34 −18 ---	41 −29 ---	45 −27 ---	47 −28 ---	53 −35 ---
54 −25 ---	62 −36 ---	76 −47 ---	84 −59 ---	43 −17 ---	95 −68 ---	73 −49 ---
64 −28 ---	52 −17 ---	85 −37 ---	94 −46 ---	78 −39 ---	43 −15 ---	87 −49 ---

From 94 take 45 = ☐   What is 24 fewer than 81 ? ☐

Take 36 from 73 ☐   Subtract 48 from 62 ☐

5

(a) Draw the hands to show the time <u>one hour later</u> than:

3 o'clock	7 o'clock	9 o'clock	12 o'clock
			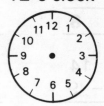

(b) Draw the hands to show the time <u>two hours later</u> than:

5 o'clock	8 o'clock	12 o'clock	1 o'clock

(c) Draw the hands to show the time <u>three hours earlier</u> than:

9 o'clock	5 o'clock	11 o'clock	3 o'clock

(d) Draw the hands to show the time $\frac{1}{2}$ hour later than:

4 o'clock	$\frac{1}{2}$ past 6	$\frac{1}{2}$ past 10	$\frac{1}{2}$ past 2

(e) Draw the hands to show the time $\frac{1}{2}$ hour earlier than:

$\frac{1}{2}$ past 5	7 o'clock	$\frac{1}{2}$ past 12	11 o'clock

Number × and ÷ (1)

(a)

| 3 | × 2 = 6 | ☐ × 3 = 9 | ☐ × 2 = 18 | ☐ × 3 = 30 |

☐ × 2 = 6   ☐ × 3 = 9   ☐ × 2 = 18   ☐ × 3 = 30

☐ × 3 = 15   ☐ × 2 = 8   ☐ × 3 = 27   ☐ × 2 = 12

☐ × 2 = 10   ☐ × 2 = 20   ☐ × 3 = 21   ☐ × 3 = 12

☐ × 3 = 18   ☐ × 3 = 24   ☐ × 2 = 14   ☐ × 2 = 16

(b)

10	11	21	23	15	14
× 2	× 3	× 2	× 3	× 2	× 3
20	☐	☐	☐	☐	☐

11	13	24	32	16	16
× 2	× 3	× 2	× 3	× 2	× 3
☐	☐	☐	☐	☐	☐

13	12	33	23	19	19
× 2	× 3	× 2	× 3	× 2	× 3
☐	☐	☐	☐	☐	☐

14	10	44	30	17	15
× 2	× 3	× 2	× 3	× 2	× 3
☐	☐	☐	☐	☐	☐

11
2)22   2)32   2)33   3)33   3)42   3)34

2)26   2)36   2)37   3)39   3)48   3)37

2)44   2)52   2)55   3)36   3)51   3)46

Two multiplied by 6 = ☐   What is twice 10? ☐

Find nine times 3 ☐   Multiply three by 8 ☐

How many twos equal 18? ☐   Divide eighteen by 3 ☐

7

12p +19p **21p**	7p +14p ___ p	16p + 8p ___ p	9p +15p ___ p	17p + 6p ___ p	5p +18p ___ p	19p + 8p ___ p
17p +26p ___ p	34p +18p ___ p	29p +15p ___ p	37p +28p ___ p	46p +19p ___ p	58p +25p ___ p	69p +28p ___ p
12p 16p +35p **63p**	14p 12p +27p ___ p	31p 15p +29p ___ p	40p 38p +17p ___ p	13p 27p +35p ___ p	8p 24p +46p ___ p	35p 27p +14p ___ p
14p 27p +39p ___ p	36p 19p +18p ___ p	25p 39p +28p ___ p	47p 18p +26p ___ p	15p 46p +19p ___ p	38p 17p +19p ___ p	29p 15p +26p ___ p

$2\frac{1}{2}$p + 3 p = $\boxed{5\frac{1}{2}}$ p

$1\frac{1}{2}$p + $2\frac{1}{2}$p = $\boxed{}$ p

$3\frac{1}{2}$p + $5\frac{1}{2}$p = $\boxed{}$ p

$4\frac{1}{2}$p + $5\frac{1}{2}$p = $\boxed{}$ p

12 p + $9\frac{1}{2}$p ___ p	$7\frac{1}{2}$p +15 p ___ p	$6\frac{1}{2}$p +$12\frac{1}{2}$p ___ p	$17\frac{1}{2}$p +$14\frac{1}{2}$p ___ p	18 p + $9\frac{1}{2}$p ___ p	$15\frac{1}{2}$p + $8\frac{1}{2}$p ___ p	$19\frac{1}{2}$p + $9\frac{1}{2}$p ___ p
16 p 24 p +$25\frac{1}{2}$p **$65\frac{1}{2}$p**	$18\frac{1}{2}$p $34\frac{1}{2}$p +26 p ___ p	$36\frac{1}{2}$p $19\frac{1}{2}$p +$24\frac{1}{2}$p ___ p	20 p $28\frac{1}{2}$p +$37\frac{1}{2}$p ___ p	$13\frac{1}{2}$p $27\frac{1}{2}$p +$48\frac{1}{2}$p ___ p	40 p $37\frac{1}{2}$p +$19\frac{1}{2}$p ___ p	$13\frac{1}{2}$p $48\frac{1}{2}$p +$26\frac{1}{2}$p ___ p

18p	27p	39p	48p	19p	67p	58p
−12p	−13p	−16p	−22p	− 5p	−31p	−30p
6p	___p	___p	___p	___p	___p	___p

20p	40p	60p	50p	70p	80p	90p
−15p	−24p	−51p	−47p	−63p	−72p	−86p
___p	___p	___p	___p	___p	___p	___p

24p	27p	32p	45p	67p	81p	73p
−16p	−18p	−26p	−37p	−58p	−72p	−65p
___p	___p	___p	___p	___p	___p	___p

$25\frac{1}{2}$	$23\frac{1}{2}$p	$27\frac{1}{2}$p	$42\frac{1}{2}$p	$55\frac{1}{2}$p	$63\frac{1}{2}$p	$76\frac{1}{2}$p
−18	−19 p	−18 p	−37 p	−28 p	−35 p	−28 p
$7\frac{1}{2}$p	___p	___p	___p	___p	___p	___p

28 p	37 p	48 p	36 p	57 p	64 p	79 p
−$14\frac{1}{2}$p	−$23\frac{1}{2}$p	−$15\frac{1}{2}$p	−$12\frac{1}{2}$p	−$33\frac{1}{2}$p	−$21\frac{1}{2}$p	−$46\frac{1}{2}$p
___p	___p	___p	___p	___p	___p	___p

53 p	36 p	49 p	27 p	44 p	77 p	55 p
−$30\frac{1}{2}$p	−$20\frac{1}{2}$p	−$10\frac{1}{2}$p	−$17\frac{1}{2}$p	−$24\frac{1}{2}$p	−$37\frac{1}{2}$p	−$15\frac{1}{2}$p
___p	___p	___p	___p	___p	___p	___p

20 p	40 p	30 p	70 p	90 p	60 p	50 p
− $7\frac{1}{2}$p	−$18\frac{1}{2}$p	−$14\frac{1}{2}$p	−$31\frac{1}{2}$p	−$45\frac{1}{2}$p	−$23\frac{1}{2}$p	−$36\frac{1}{2}$p
___p	___p	___p	___p	___p	___p	___p

Number × and ÷ (1)

3	× 4 = 12		× 5 = 30		× 6 = 48		× 5 = 35
	× 5 = 15		× 6 = 36		× 4 = 20		× 4 = 36
	× 6 = 18		× 4 = 32		× 5 = 45		× 5 = 50
	× 4 = 24		× 5 = 25		× 6 = 60		× 6 = 54

$$\begin{array}{r} 11 \\ \times\ 4 \\ \hline \mathbf{44} \end{array}$$
$$\begin{array}{r} 13 \\ \times\ 4 \\ \hline \end{array}$$
$$\begin{array}{r} 11 \\ \times\ 5 \\ \hline \end{array}$$
$$\begin{array}{r} 14 \\ \times\ 5 \\ \hline \end{array}$$
$$\begin{array}{r} 10 \\ \times\ 6 \\ \hline \end{array}$$
$$\begin{array}{r} 14 \\ \times\ 6 \\ \hline \end{array}$$

$$\begin{array}{r} 12 \\ \times\ 4 \\ \hline \end{array}$$
$$\begin{array}{r} 23 \\ \times\ 4 \\ \hline \end{array}$$
$$\begin{array}{r} 12 \\ \times\ 5 \\ \hline \end{array}$$
$$\begin{array}{r} 16 \\ \times\ 5 \\ \hline \end{array}$$
$$\begin{array}{r} 11 \\ \times\ 6 \\ \hline \end{array}$$
$$\begin{array}{r} 15 \\ \times\ 6 \\ \hline \end{array}$$

$$\begin{array}{r} 21 \\ \times\ 4 \\ \hline \end{array}$$
$$\begin{array}{r} 16 \\ \times\ 4 \\ \hline \end{array}$$
$$\begin{array}{r} 15 \\ \times\ 5 \\ \hline \end{array}$$
$$\begin{array}{r} 17 \\ \times\ 5 \\ \hline \end{array}$$
$$\begin{array}{r} 12 \\ \times\ 6 \\ \hline \end{array}$$
$$\begin{array}{r} 16 \\ \times\ 6 \\ \hline \end{array}$$

$$\begin{array}{r} 20 \\ \times\ 4 \\ \hline \end{array}$$
$$\begin{array}{r} 18 \\ \times\ 4 \\ \hline \end{array}$$
$$\begin{array}{r} 13 \\ \times\ 5 \\ \hline \end{array}$$
$$\begin{array}{r} 19 \\ \times\ 5 \\ \hline \end{array}$$
$$\begin{array}{r} 13 \\ \times\ 6 \\ \hline \end{array}$$
$$\begin{array}{r} 17 \\ \times\ 6 \\ \hline \end{array}$$

11
$4\overline{)44}$ $4\overline{)45}$ $5\overline{)55}$ $5\overline{)70}$ $6\overline{)66}$ $6\overline{)71}$

$4\overline{)48}$ $4\overline{)49}$ $5\overline{)45}$ $5\overline{)63}$ $6\overline{)48}$ $6\overline{)75}$

$4\overline{)25}$ $4\overline{)53}$ $5\overline{)56}$ $5\overline{)74}$ $6\overline{)25}$ $6\overline{)84}$

$4\overline{)33}$ $4\overline{)62}$ $5\overline{)38}$ $5\overline{)79}$ $6\overline{)33}$ $6\overline{)92}$

$4\overline{)26}$ $4\overline{)67}$ $5\overline{)47}$ $5\overline{)83}$ $6\overline{)52}$ $6\overline{)78}$

Fractions

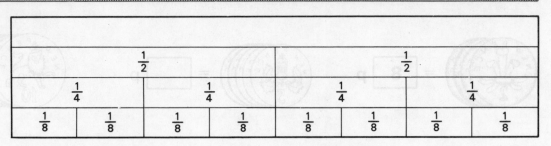

ONE WHOLE ONE

one half

one quarter

one eighth

	$\frac{1}{2}$			$\frac{1}{2}$	
$\frac{1}{4}$	$\frac{1}{4}$	$\frac{1}{4}$		$\frac{1}{4}$	
$\frac{1}{8}$	$\frac{1}{8}$	$\frac{1}{8}$	$\frac{1}{8}$	$\frac{1}{8}$	$\frac{1}{8}$	$\frac{1}{8}$	$\frac{1}{8}$

What fraction of each of the shapes is shaded? Not shaded?

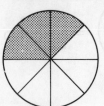
$\boxed{\frac{3}{8}}$ **shaded**

$\boxed{\frac{5}{8}}$ **not shaded**

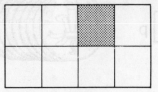
$\boxed{-}$ shaded

$\boxed{-}$ not shaded

$\boxed{-}$ shaded

$\boxed{-}$ not shaded

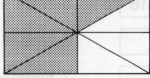
$\boxed{-}$ shaded

$\boxed{-}$ not shaded

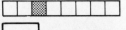
$\boxed{-}$ shaded

$\boxed{-}$ not shaded

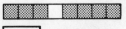
$\boxed{-}$ shaded

$\boxed{-}$ not shaded

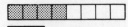
$\boxed{-}$ shaded

$\boxed{-}$ not shaded

How many eighths?

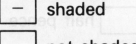

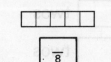

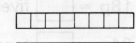

$\boxed{\frac{8}{8}}$

$\boxed{\frac{}{8}}$

$\boxed{\frac{}{8}}$

$\boxed{\frac{}{8}}$

$\boxed{\frac{}{8}}$

shade $\frac{1}{8}$ of the drawing

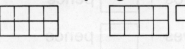

shade $\frac{3}{8}$ of the drawing

shade $\frac{5}{8}$ of the drawing

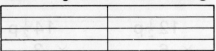

shade $\frac{7}{8}$ of the drawing

$1\frac{1}{4} = \boxed{\frac{5}{4}}$ $1\frac{1}{8} = \boxed{\frac{}{8}}$ $1\frac{3}{4} = \boxed{\frac{}{4}}$ $\frac{7}{4} = \boxed{}$ $\frac{17}{8} = \boxed{}$ $\frac{15}{4} = \boxed{}$

$\frac{1}{2} + \frac{1}{4}$ $\boxed{\frac{3}{4}}$ $\frac{1}{4} + \frac{3}{8} = \boxed{}$ $\frac{1}{2} + \frac{1}{8} = \boxed{}$ $\frac{1}{8} + \frac{1}{4} = \boxed{}$ $\frac{3}{4} + \frac{1}{8} = \boxed{}$

$1 - \frac{1}{2} = \boxed{}$ $1 - \frac{1}{4} = \boxed{}$ $1 - \frac{1}{8} = \boxed{}$ $1 - \frac{3}{4} = \boxed{}$ $1 - \frac{3}{8} = \boxed{}$

Money – how much?

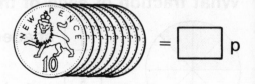

= | 8 | p   = | | p   = | | p

= | | p   = | | p   = | | p

3 twos + 2 fives = | 16 | p   5 twos + 3 ones = | | 3 tens + 4 twos = | |

4 fives + 4 twos = | | 6 tens + 3 twos = | | 8 twos + 3 fives = | |

3 tens + 6 fives = | | 7 twos + 4 fives = | | 5 fives + 5 tens = | |

11p = | 1 | **ten** + | 1 | **one** $11\frac{1}{2}$p = | | ten + | | half pence

15p = | | ten + | | five $17\frac{1}{2}$p = | | fives + | | half pence

18p = | | fives + | | ones   19p = | | twos + | | pence

24p = | | tens + | | twos   23p = | | fives + | | pence

38p = | | tens + | | twos   80p = | | tens + | | twos

13 p	15 p	14 p	15 p	14 p	16 p
× 2	× 3	× 4	× 5	× 6	× 4
26 p	___ p	___ p	___ p	___ p	___ p

$11\frac{1}{2}$p	$11\frac{1}{2}$p	$12\frac{1}{2}$p	$11\frac{1}{2}$p	$12\frac{1}{2}$p	$14\frac{1}{2}$p
× 2	× 4	× 3	× 5	× 6	× 3
___ p	___ p	___ p	___ p	___ p	___ p

$16\frac{1}{2}$p	$21\frac{1}{2}$p	$17\frac{1}{2}$p	$15\frac{1}{2}$p	$23\frac{1}{2}$p	$32\frac{1}{2}$p
× 6	× 4	× 2	× 5	× 4	× 3
___ p	___ p	___ p	___ p	___ p	___ p

12

Money ÷

4p

2) 8p	3) 9p	4) 12p	5) 10p	6) 12p
2) 12p	3) 12p	4) 18p	5) 25p	6) 24p
2) 20p	3) 21p	4) 32p	5) 40p	6) 36p
2) 18p	3) 18p	4) 24p	5) 35p	6) 48p
2) 14p	3) 27p	4) 36p	5) 45p	6) 54p

11p

2) 22p	4) 44p	6) 66p	3) 33p	5) 55p
2) 28p	3) 39p	4) 48p	3) 36p	2) 26p

16p

2) 32p	3) 45p	5) 65p	6) 72p	5) 75p
2) 38p	4) 56p	3) 51p	4) 68p	6) 84p

$6\frac{1}{2}$p

2) 13p	2) 19p	4) 54p	4) 58p	6) 75p
3) $19\frac{1}{2}$p	3) $34\frac{1}{2}$p	5) $57\frac{1}{2}$p	5) $67\frac{1}{2}$p	3) $52\frac{1}{2}$p
6) 87p	5) $87\frac{1}{2}$p	6) 93p	2) 21p	3) $88\frac{1}{2}$p

13

Time (2)

(a) Write the times shown on these clocks:

$\frac{1}{4}$ past 7

_____

_____

_____

(b) On each of these clocks draw the hands to show the time:

$\frac{1}{4}$ to 4

$\frac{1}{4}$ past 6

$\frac{1}{4}$ to 10

$\frac{1}{4}$ past 1

(c) Here are four clocks:

A

B

C

D

How much time has passed from

Clock A to Clock B? $\boxed{2\frac{1}{2}}$ Clock A to Clock C? $\boxed{}$

Clock A to Clock D? $\boxed{}$ Clock B to Clock C? $\boxed{}$

Clock B to Clock D? $\boxed{}$ Clock C to Clock D? $\boxed{}$

(d) Write the times shown on these clocks:

5 past 3

14

Complete the table chart below very carefully.

Table	1	2	3	4	5	6	7	8	9	10
twos 2s	2	4	6	8	10	12				
threes 3s	3	6	9	12	15					
fours 4s	4	8	12	16						
fives 5s	5	10								
sixes 6s	6									

Speed tests

3 × 4 = ☐	5 × 5 = ☐	9 × 3 = ☐	9 × 6 = ☐
6 × 2 = ☐	7 × 3 = ☐	8 × 5 = ☐	9 × 4 = ☐
5 × 3 = ☐	6 × 6 = ☐	9 × 4 = ☐	5 × 2 = ☐
3 × 6 = ☐	9 × 2 = ☐	8 × 6 = ☐	10 × 5 = ☐
4 × 4 = ☐	8 × 4 = ☐	7 × 2 = ☐	8 × 3 = ☐
6 ÷ 3 = ☐	21 ÷ 3 = ☐	24 ÷ 6 = ☐	28 ÷ 4 = ☐
12 ÷ 2 = ☐	25 ÷ 5 = ☐	40 ÷ 4 = ☐	15 ÷ 3 = ☐
15 ÷ 5 = ☐	32 ÷ 4 = ☐	16 ÷ 2 = ☐	54 ÷ 6 = ☐

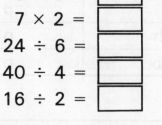

(4×2) +1 = **9**	(3×3) +2 = ☐	(2×5) +4 = ☐	(3×6) +3 = ☐
(5×3) +1 = ☐	(4×5) +3 = ☐	(10×2) +1 = ☐	(9×4) +2 = ☐
(4×4) +2 = ☐	(8×2) +1 = ☐	(6×6) +4 = ☐	(8×5) +4 = ☐
(5×5) +3 = ☐	(7×6) +4 = ☐	(8×4) +3 = ☐	(10×3) +2 = ☐

8 ÷ 2 = ☐	13 ÷ 2 = ☐ rem ☐	42 ÷ 5 = ☐ rem ☐	
9 ÷ 2 = ☐ rem ☐	16 ÷ 3 = ☐ rem ☐	28 ÷ 3 = ☐ rem ☐	
12 ÷ 3 = ☐	18 ÷ 4 = ☐ rem ☐	15 ÷ 2 = ☐ rem ☐	
13 ÷ 3 = ☐ rem ☐	23 ÷ 5 = ☐ rem ☐	32 ÷ 6 = ☐ rem ☐	
16 ÷ 4 = ☐	26 ÷ 6 = ☐ rem ☐	29 ÷ 4 = ☐ rem ☐	
17 ÷ 4 = ☐ rem ☐	19 ÷ 2 = ☐ rem ☐	22 ÷ 3 = ☐ rem ☐	
10 ÷ 2 = ☐	14 ÷ 5 = ☐ rem ☐	57 ÷ 6 = ☐ rem ☐	
11 ÷ 2 = ☐ rem ☐	23 ÷ 3 = ☐ rem ☐	17 ÷ 2 = ☐ rem ☐	

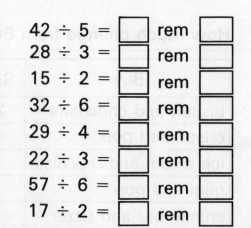

(a)

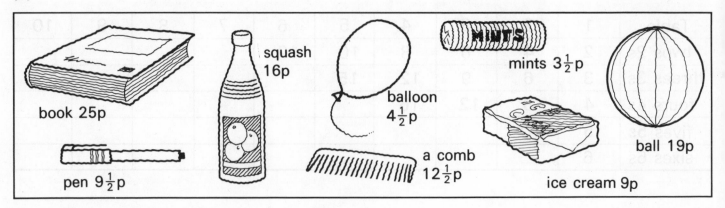

book 25p
pen $9\frac{1}{2}$p
squash 16p
balloon $4\frac{1}{2}$p
a comb $12\frac{1}{2}$p
mints $3\frac{1}{2}$p
ice cream 9p
ball 19p

Buy	Spend
balloon and mints	**8** p
comb and ice cream	p
ball and mints	p
pen and squash	p
book and comb	p

Buy	Spend
3 balloons	p
6 mints	p
4 ice creams	p
5 pens	p
3 squash	p

(b)

bar chocolate 24p
biscuit 5p
gum $6\frac{1}{2}$p
pop $15\frac{1}{2}$p
ice cream $7\frac{1}{2}$p
crunch bar 17p
fizzer 13p
crisps 8p

How much change from 50p when you buy:

Buy	Spend	Change
biscuit and chocolate	**29p**	**21p**
crisps and pop		
ice cream and chocolate		
gum and pop		
crunch bar and fizzer		

Buy	Spend	Change
6 biscuits		
4 gums		
5 crisps		
2 pop		
3 fizzers		

This shows:
1 hundred, 5 tens and 5 ones.

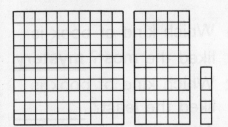

Write the number shown in each of these:

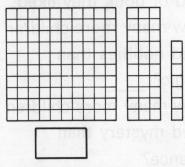

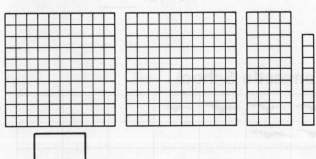

Complete:

138 = | 1 | hundreds | 3 | tens | 8 | ones

230 = [ ] hundreds [ ] tens [ ] ones

452 = [ ] hundreds [ ] tens [ ] ones

506 = [ ] hundreds [ ] tens [ ] ones

Write these numbers:

h	t	o
2	4	1

two hundred and forty-one

four hundred and sixty-five

three hundred and twenty

seven hundred and fifty

nine hundred and six

eight hundred and fifty

Write in figures the numbers shown on each abacus:

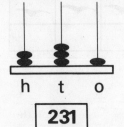
h t o
231

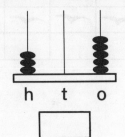
h t o
[ ]

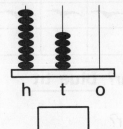
h t o
[ ]

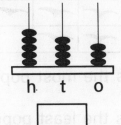
h t o
[ ]

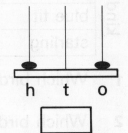
h t o
[ ]

Show each of these numbers on an abacus:

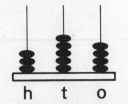
h t o
three hundred and fifty-four

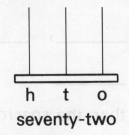
h t o
seventy-two

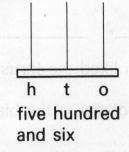
h t o
five hundred and six

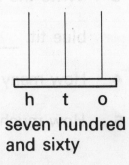
h t o
seven hundred and sixty

Graphs

This graph shows the kind of books liked the most by children in Tencastle School.

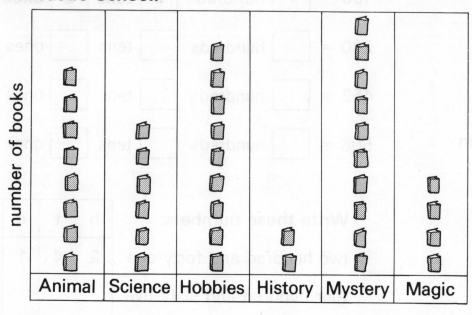

number of books

| Animal | Science | Hobbies | History | Mystery | Magic |

1. Which kind of book is liked the most? **mystery**
2. Which kind of book is liked the least? _____
3. Altogether ____ children were asked to say which kind of book they liked.
4. How many more children liked hobbies than magic? ____
5. How many more children liked mystery than science? ____

Favourite garden birds liked by children in Tencastle School.

kinds of birds													
robin	✓	✓	✓	✓	✓	✓	✓	✓	✓				
thrush	✓	✓	✓	✓	✓	✓	✓						
sparrow	✓	✓	✓	✓									
blackbird	✓	✓	✓	✓	✓	✓	✓						
blue tit	✓	✓	✓	✓	✓	✓	✓	✓	✓	✓	✓	✓	✓
starling	✓	✓											

1. Which bird is the most popular? **blue tit**

2. Which bird is the least popular? _____

3. Write the birds in order beginning with the most popular.

   blue tit, _____, _____, _____, _____, _____.

4. How many children liked the thrush best? _____

5. How much more popular is the blackbird than the sparrow? _____

18

346	263	455	503	733	626
22	112	223	164	124	241
+121	+424	+121	+232	+132	+122
489					

335	244	132	237	349	128
243	526	648	456	225	356
+313	+125	+116	+303	+424	+513

232	340	524	605	263	452
144	285	171	182	374	196
+ 33	+123	+252	+191	+261	+250

57	48	29	47	23	37
44	75	37	54	56	95
+63	+54	+93	+68	+89	+66

75	48	75	98	65	87
87	57	39	87	95	96
+66	+69	+58	+76	+88	+59

269	477	604	426	290	423
355	243	187	295	369	177
+142	+186	+155	+267	+238	+359

Money – shopping 2

(a) Models

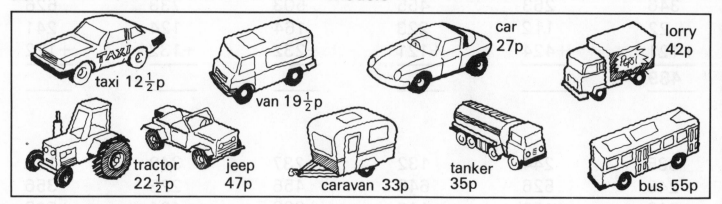

taxi 12½p   van 19½p   car 27p   lorry 42p

tractor 22½p   jeep 47p   caravan 33p   tanker 35p   bus 55p

How much to buy:

Buy	Spend
lorry and jeep	**89 p**
bus and tanker	p
tractor and caravan	p
van and taxi	p
car and lorry	p

Buy	Spend
4 taxis	p
3 tractors	p
2 jeeps	p
3 caravans	p
3 cars	p

(b)

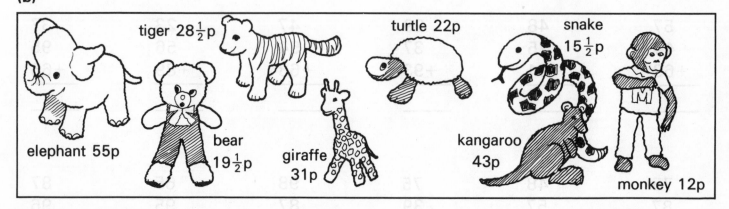

tiger 28½p   turtle 22p   snake 15½p

elephant 55p   bear 19½p   giraffe 31p   kangaroo 43p   monkey 12p

How much change from £1.00 when you buy:

Buy	Spend	Change
elephant	**55 p**	**45 p**
turtle	p	p
snake	p	p
kangaroo and tiger	p	p
bear and giraffe	p	p

Buy	Spend	Change
7 monkeys	p	p
2 kangaroos	p	p
4 snakes	p	p
5 bears	p	p
4 turtles	p	p

538 −415 **123**	675 −353	759 −247	846 −424	972 −651	483 −172
546 −136	675 −345	484 −254	764 −362	826 −524	983 −673
256 −136	394 −170	532 −210	648 −320	582 −101	427 −205
324 −110	545 −245	637 −407	863 −352	495 −205	742 −640
550 −235	390 −168	830 −514	670 −327	980 −543	760 −219
205 −183	406 −272	703 −441	502 −151	908 −666	807 −314
700 −325	400 −116	800 −628	600 −439	300 −157	500 −418
430 −253	542 −161	904 −782	658 −374	375 −193	723 −502

Number × (below 1000)

(a)

312	233	212	423	313	221
× 2	× 3	× 4	× 2	× 3	× 4
624					

204	302	102	402	203	201
× 2	× 3	× 4	× 2	× 3	× 4

(b)

206	205	103	407	306	204
× 2	× 3	× 4	× 2	× 3	× 4
412					

108	107	208	109	109	209
× 6	× 5	× 4	× 6	× 5	× 4

(c)

216	226	124	117	113	317
× 2	× 3	× 4	× 5	× 6	× 2
232					

327	217	119	114	117	116
× 3	× 4	× 5	× 6	× 4	× 6

(d)

174	263	132	131	121	483
× 2	× 3	× 4	× 5	× 6	× 2
348					

273	131	394	242	141	152
× 3	× 6	× 2	× 4	× 6	× 3

(e)

145	134	289	256	143	286
× 3	× 4	× 2	× 3	× 4	× 3
435					

Linear measurement (cm, ½cm)

Measure these ten lines and write the length of the lines in the table below.

Line	A	B	C	D	E	F	G	H	I	J
Length	**4 cm**									

A ——————————

B ——————————————

C ————

D ————————————

E ——————————

F ———————————————

G ——————————

H ——————————————

I ———————————————

J ——————————————————

What is the difference in length between these lines?

A and B [**3**] cm   C and D [ ] cm   D and B [ ] cm   E and H [ ] cm

What is the total length of these lines?

B and A [ ] cm   C and B [ ] cm   D and C [ ] cm   C, E and A [ ] cm

F and C [ ] cm   G and E [ ] cm   J and D [ ] cm   G, D and F [ ] cm

Measure these shapes:

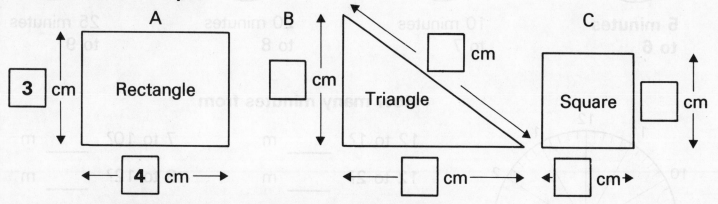

A   Rectangle   [**3**] cm   [**4**] cm →

B   Triangle   [ ] cm   [ ] cm →

C   Square   [ ] cm   [ ] cm →

The distance all round each shape is the PERIMETER.

Perimeter of A = [**14**] cm   Perimeter of B = [ ] cm   Perimeter of C = [ ] cm

Draw lines which measure:

3 cm   9½ cm

(a) On each of these clocks draw the hands to show the time.

5 minutes past 8   10 minutes past 10   20 minutes past 2   25 minutes past 9

(b) Write the times shown on these clocks.

5 minutes to 8

(c) On each of these clocks draw the hands to show the time.

 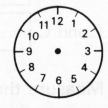 

5 minutes to 6   10 minutes to 7   20 minutes to 8   25 minutes to 9

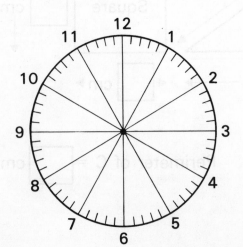

How many minutes from

12 to 1?	____ m	7 to 10?	____ m
12 to 2?	____ m	8 to 12?	____ m
1 to 4?	____ m	4 to 6?	____ m
1 to 6?	____ m	6 to 10?	____ m
2 to 5?	____ m	10 to 12?	____ m
5 to 9?	____ m	12 to 5?	____ m

(a)   **112**

$2\overline{)224}$ $3\overline{)336}$ $4\overline{)448}$ $5\overline{)555}$ $6\overline{)666}$

(b)   **41**

$3\overline{)123}$ $3\overline{)155}$ $3\overline{)189}$ $5\overline{)155}$ $6\overline{)186}$

$2\overline{)122}$ $2\overline{)182}$ $6\overline{)246}$ $4\overline{)248}$ $6\overline{)366}$

(c)   **117**

$2\overline{)234}$ $3\overline{)348}$ $4\overline{)456}$ $2\overline{)278}$ $3\overline{)342}$

$2\overline{)456}$ $3\overline{)678}$ $5\overline{)565}$ $6\overline{)684}$ $4\overline{)464}$

(d)   **135**

$5\overline{)675}$ $6\overline{)744}$ $4\overline{)792}$ $3\overline{)768}$ $6\overline{)882}$

$3\overline{)867}$ $4\overline{)996}$ $5\overline{)845}$ $6\overline{)954}$ $5\overline{)975}$

(e)   **178 r 1**

$2\overline{)357}$ $3\overline{)446}$ $4\overline{)515}$ $5\overline{)648}$ $6\overline{)754}$

$4\overline{)654}$ $6\overline{)875}$ $2\overline{)573}$ $5\overline{)894}$ $3\overline{)77}$

$4\overline{)735}$ $5\overline{)972}$ $6\overline{)987}$ $3\overline{)863}$ $2\overline{)959}$

(f)   **208**

$2\overline{)416}$ $3\overline{)960}$ $4\overline{)816}$ $5\overline{)525}$ $6\overline{)648}$

$2\overline{)280}$ $3\overline{)390}$ $4\overline{)840}$ $5\overline{)550}$ $4\overline{)480}$

$2\overline{)600}$ $3\overline{)600}$ $4\overline{)800}$ $2\overline{)340}$ $3\overline{)480}$

= **65** p    = ___ p

 = ___ p    = ___ p

 = ___ p    = ___ p

£1.00 = 100p

£2.00 = ___ p   £4.00 = ___ p   £6.00 = ___ p   £10.00 = ___ p

300p = £ ___   500p = £ ___   800p = £ ___   700p = £ ___

£1.28 =  +

£1.28 = £1 and 28p

£1.37 = £ _1_ and _37_ p   £0.63 = £ ___ and ___ p

£6.86 = £ ___ and ___ p   £8.05 = £ ___ and ___ p

£1.10
___

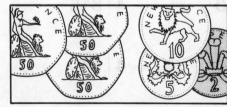
___

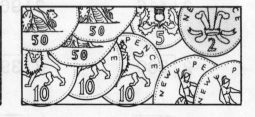
___

26

Fractions

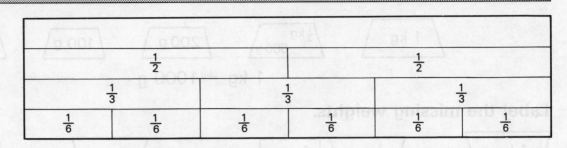

ONE WHOLE ONE

one half

one third

one sixth

What fraction or part of the shapes are shaded?

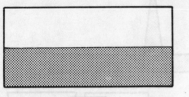 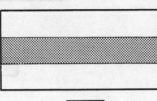 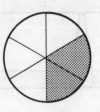 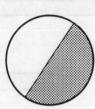

$\frac{1}{2}$ $\boxed{-}$ $\boxed{-}$ $\boxed{-}$

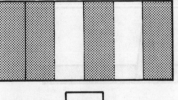 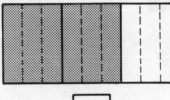 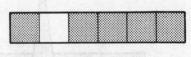

$\boxed{-}$ $\boxed{-}$ $\boxed{-}$

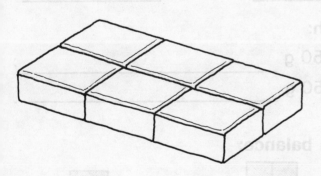

There are $\boxed{}$ squares of toffee.

There are $\boxed{}$ squares in $\frac{1}{2}$ of the toffee.

There are $\boxed{}$ squares in $\frac{1}{3}$ of the toffee.

There are $\boxed{}$ squares in $\frac{1}{6}$ of the toffee.

$1\frac{1}{3} = \boxed{\frac{4}{3}}$ $2\frac{1}{3} = \boxed{\frac{}{3}}$ $3\frac{2}{3} = \boxed{\frac{}{3}}$ $1\frac{1}{6} = \boxed{\frac{}{6}}$ $1\frac{5}{6} = \boxed{\frac{}{6}}$ $2\frac{1}{6} = \boxed{\frac{}{6}}$

$\frac{1}{1} = \boxed{1}$ $\frac{5}{2} = \boxed{}$ $\frac{4}{3} = \boxed{}$ $\frac{6}{3} = \boxed{}$ $\frac{7}{6} = \boxed{}$ $\frac{2}{3} = \boxed{\frac{}{6}}$

$\frac{1}{3}$ of 12p $= \boxed{4}$ p $\frac{2}{3}$ of 12p $= \boxed{}$ $\frac{1}{6}$ of 12p $= \boxed{}$ $\frac{5}{6}$ of 12p $= \boxed{}$

$\frac{1}{3}$ of 18p $= \boxed{}$ p $\frac{2}{3}$ of 18p $= \boxed{}$ $\frac{1}{6}$ of 18p $= \boxed{}$ $\frac{5}{6}$ of 18p $= \boxed{}$

Mass

| 1 kg | ½ kg 500 g | 200 g | 100 g | 50 g |

1 kg = 1000 g

Label the missing weights.

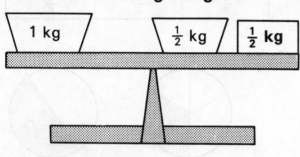

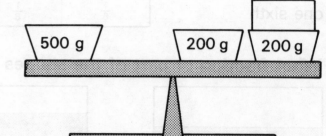

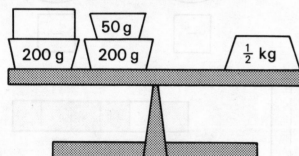

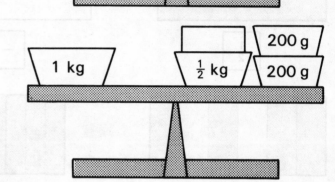

2 **Which 2 weights would you use to weigh:**

150 g __**100 g, 50 g**__ ; 550 g _____ ; 700 g _____ .

3 **Which 3 weights would you use to weigh:**

350 g __**100 g, 200 g, 50 g**__ ; 750 g _____ ;

800 g _____ ; 650 g _____

4 **Write the weights shown on each spring balance:**

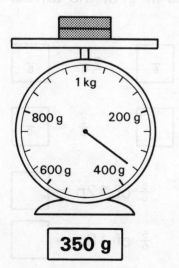

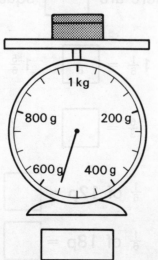

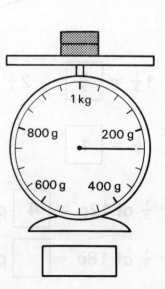

350 g

28

Shopping mixed

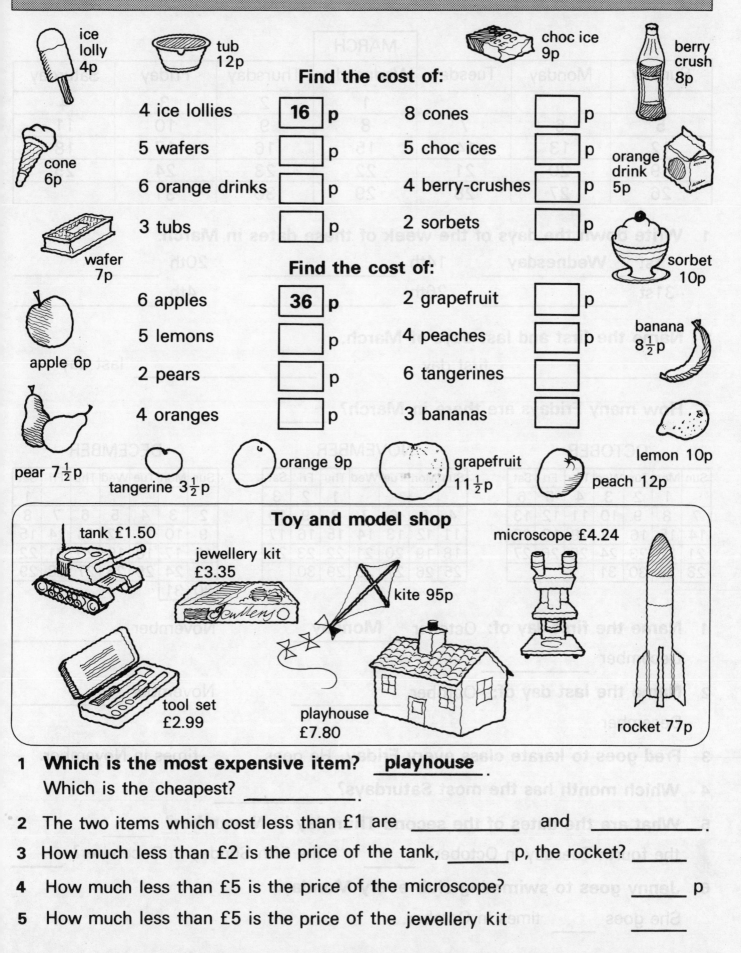

ice lolly 4p

tub 12p

choc ice 9p

berry crush 8p

cone 6p

orange drink 5p

Find the cost of:

4 ice lollies	**16** p	8 cones	☐ p
5 wafers	☐ p	5 choc ices	☐ p
6 orange drinks	☐ p	4 berry-crushes	☐ p
3 tubs	☐ p	2 sorbets	☐ p

wafer 7p

sorbet 10p

Find the cost of:

6 apples	**36** p	2 grapefruit	☐ p
5 lemons	☐ p	4 peaches	☐ p
2 pears	☐ p	6 tangerines	☐
4 oranges	☐ p	3 bananas	☐

apple 6p

banana $8\frac{1}{2}$p

pear $7\frac{1}{2}$p

tangerine $3\frac{1}{2}$p

orange 9p

grapefruit $11\frac{1}{2}$p

lemon 10p

peach 12p

Toy and model shop

tank £1.50

jewellery kit £3.35

kite 95p

microscope £4.24

tool set £2.99

playhouse £7.80

rocket 77p

1 **Which is the most expensive item?** ___playhouse___ .

Which is the cheapest? _____ .

2 The two items which cost less than £1 are _____ and _____ .

3 How much less than £2 is the price of the tank, _____ p, the rocket? _____

4 How much less than £5 is the price of the microscope? _____ p

5 How much less than £5 is the price of the jewellery kit _____

Time (4)

			MARCH			
Sunday	Monday	Tuesday	Wednesday	Thursday	Friday	Saturday
			1	2	3	4
5	6	7	8	9	10	11
12	13	14	15	16	17	18
19	20	21	22	23	24	25
26	27	28	29	30	31	

1 Write down the days of the week of these dates in March.

1st **Wednesday**   14th _____   20th _____

31st _____   26th _____   4th _____

2 Name the first and last days of March.

_____ first day   _____ last day

3 How many Fridays are there in March? _____

OCTOBER

Sun	Mon	Tue	Wed	Thu	Fri	Sat
	1	2	3	4	5	6
7	8	9	10	11	12	13
14	15	16	17	18	19	20
21	22	23	24	25	26	27
28	29	30	31			

NOVEMBER

Sun	Mon	Tue	Wed	Thu	Fri	Sat
				1	2	3
4	5	6	7	8	9	10
11	12	13	14	15	16	17
18	19	20	21	22	23	24
25	26	27	28	29	30	

DECEMBER

Sun	Mon	Tue	Wed	Thu	Fri	Sat
						1
2	3	4	5	6	7	8
9	10	11	12	13	14	15
16	17	18	19	20	21	22
23	24	25	26	27	28	29
30	31					

1 Name the first day of: October **Monday**   November _____

December _____

2 Name the last day of: October _____   November _____

December _____

3 Fred goes to karate class every Friday. He goes _____ times in November.

4 Which month has the most Saturdays? _____

5 What are the dates of the second Thursday in November? _____

the fourth Tuesday in October? _____   the fifth Sunday in December? _____

6 Jenny goes to swimming club every Monday.

She goes _____ times in October.

Fractions

1 Whole							
$\frac{1}{2}$				$\frac{1}{2}$			
$\frac{1}{4}$		$\frac{1}{4}$		$\frac{1}{4}$		$\frac{1}{4}$	
$\frac{1}{8}$	$\frac{1}{8}$	$\frac{1}{8}$	$\frac{1}{8}$	$\frac{1}{8}$	$\frac{1}{8}$	$\frac{1}{8}$	$\frac{1}{8}$
$\frac{1}{3}$		$\frac{1}{3}$			$\frac{1}{3}$		
$\frac{1}{6}$	$\frac{1}{6}$	$\frac{1}{6}$		$\frac{1}{6}$	$\frac{1}{6}$		$\frac{1}{6}$

What fraction of each shape is (a) shaded (b) not shaded?

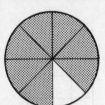

$\boxed{\frac{7}{8}}$ **shaded**

$\boxed{\frac{1}{8}}$ **not shaded**

$\boxed{}$ shaded

$\boxed{}$ not shaded

$\boxed{}$ shaded

$\boxed{}$ not shaded

shade $\frac{1}{3}$ of the drawing

shade $\frac{3}{8}$ of the drawing

shade $\frac{1}{6}$ of the drawing

shade $\frac{1}{2}$ of the drawing

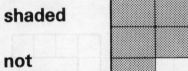

 $= \frac{20}{8}$

 $= \frac{}{3}$

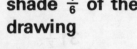
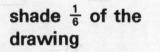

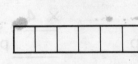 $= \frac{}{4}$

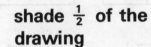

$2\frac{1}{2} = \boxed{\frac{10}{4}}$ $5\frac{1}{3} = \boxed{\frac{}{3}}$ $2\frac{5}{6} = \boxed{\frac{}{6}}$ $2\frac{3}{4} = \boxed{\frac{}{8}}$ $3\frac{1}{2} = \boxed{\frac{}{4}}$

$\frac{22}{3} = \boxed{7\frac{1}{3}}$ $\frac{37}{8} = \boxed{}$ $\frac{18}{4} = \boxed{}$ $\frac{15}{6} = \boxed{}$ $\frac{32}{3} = \boxed{}$

$\frac{3}{8} + \frac{1}{4} = \boxed{\frac{5}{8}}$ $\frac{5}{6} + \frac{1}{6} = \boxed{}$ $\frac{1}{4} + \frac{1}{2} = \boxed{}$ $\frac{2}{3} + \frac{1}{6} = \boxed{}$

$\frac{3}{4}$ of 20p $= \boxed{}$ $\frac{5}{6}$ of 60p $= \boxed{}$ $\frac{1}{2}$ of 48p $= \boxed{}$ $\frac{2}{3}$ of 24p $= \boxed{}$

31

How many grams (g) are there in $1\frac{1}{2}$ kilograms (kg)? ☐ g

How many toffee bars each weighing 100 g would weigh 1 kg? ☐ bars

How many tubs of margarine weighing 250 g would weigh 1 kg? ☐ tubs

Write these in order of size starting with the smallest.

$1\frac{1}{2}$ kg   500 g   1700 g   1 kg and 80 g   350 g

_____ , _____ , _____ , _____ , _____ .

Shade $\frac{1}{6}$ of each whole one.

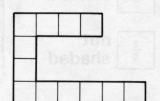
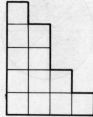

$17\frac{1}{2}$
$\times\ 5$
_____ p

$14\frac{1}{2}$
$\times\ 4$
_____ p

$31\frac{1}{2}$
$\times\ 3$
_____ p

$3\,\overline{)43\frac{1}{2}p}$ p

$6\,\overline{)75p}$ p

$4\,\overline{)54p}$ p

$16\frac{1}{2}$ p
$27\frac{1}{2}$ p
$+18$ p
_____ p

$25\frac{1}{2}$ p
$28\frac{1}{2}$ p
$+39\frac{1}{2}$ p
_____ p

48 p
$-24\frac{1}{2}$ p
_____ p

63 p
$-40\frac{1}{2}$ p
_____ p

90 p
$-66\frac{1}{2}$ p
_____ p

From 93 take 46 ☐   Take 38 from 82 ☐   Subtract 37 from 71 ☐

643
-218
_____

857
-665
_____

245
$\times\ 3$
_____

165
$\times\ 5$
_____

246
$\times\ 4$
_____

$3\,\overline{)604}$ $4\,\overline{)631}$ $5\,\overline{)535}$ $6\,\overline{)699}$ $6\,\overline{)507}$

© 1980 Ruth Dixon
First published 1980
Published by Macmillan Education Ltd
London and Basingstoke

Designed by Oxford Illustrators Ltd
Printed in Hong Kong
ISBN 0 333 30948 0